Virtual Unreality

Taylor Sapp

Alphabet Publishing

Cover Image: Halfpoint, Depositphotos

Adapted by Walton Burns

Contents

Before You Read

1. What does Virtual Reality or VR mean?

2. What are examples of things we can do through VR?

3. What are the advantages and disadvantages of VR technology?

4. Someday we may have VR rooms that can look like any place on Earth. Would you like a VR room or not?

Virtual Unreality

"SCHOOL TIME"

Aziz was late for school again! His computer, Alvin, was warning him that it was time to start. Alvin was an AI, an artificially intelligent computer. It acted like his personal assistant.

"Alvin, set my pod to morning cleaning mode," Aziz said.

"Aziz, you are already 3 minutes late to your first period class, Physical Education. There is no time for morning cleaning."

"Fine! Set my pod to school gym mode," Aziz said. Aziz's entire apartment was one room called a pod. The pod was controlled by Alvin. It was made out of a special material that could transform into any shape such as a bed, chair, or table. The floor could change into a smooth surface or a soft one like carpet. It could move so that he could run. It could even turn into a drain. A shower came out of the ceiling so he could wash.

And the walls could look like any place in the world. At night, Aziz's room looked like an ordinary teenage boy's bedroom. The walls were blue. He had posters of movie stars on the wall. He even had a window with a virtual view of outside. When the pod changed to school mode, the walls changed too.

Now the pod looked like a gym in a school. The walls looked like white painted bricks. The floor looked like a basketball court floor.

A panel opened. There was a breakfast drink inside, created by Alvin. Aziz drank it quickly. Today, it tasted like pancakes, but it came in many flavors. All meals, all classes, even every bathroom trip was done in pod. People could leave if they wanted, but most people didn't want to. The pods gave you everything you needed and more! Aziz could only think of one reason to leave. Inside the pods you were safe from everything, except possibly an angry teacher. Coach Botha, the PE teacher, was strict. He would make him run lots of extra laps if he was late! Aziz could only think of one reason to leave: Hinata.

"Sport avatar," Aziz told Alvin. Just as the pod could look like anything, avatars let you look like anything. Aziz's sport avatar wore a tank-top in the school colors, white and green, and sports shorts. It was his real face. But the sport avatar was fitter than Aziz in real life. Some kids really over did it. There was no way that Luis was 6 foot 6 inches or that he had 20 inch muscles!

Once Aziz's avatar was on, he turned on the camera and video screen and joined physical education class.

Luckily Coach Botha was absent. In his place was an AI Construct, a computer-created person that looked like Coach Botha. The Construct had his short black hair, square face, dark skin, light brown eyes, and fit body. The construct was labelled Botha-116 AIC. Constructs were AI computer programs. They were supposed to be clearly labelled AIC. This is because it isn't always easy to tell the difference between a real person's avatar and an AIC. AICs were normally in virtual reality decorations. For example, a popular restaurant mode for the pods had some AICs in the background, acting like waiters and other customers. They made the place feel more real. AICs could also be used to appear while a recorded speech was talking. They were perfect for presentations, commercials, and substitute teaching!

Coach Botha had recorded a speech that was now playing. Botha-116 AIC was moving its mouth and hands while the speech played. "Today's warm-up run is a beach run through Koh Samui beach in Thailand."

The floor of the pod changed. Aziz could feel the soft, warm feeling of sand. Or so he imagined. He'd never actually touched real sand before. The temperature of pod began to rise and the walls showed a scene of a beautiful blue ocean and a sunny sky. On his left, a rainforest and the sounds of tropical birds and even monkeys.

The run in the hot virtual sun made Aziz break into a nice sweat. They did some more stretches and exercises. Then they had a 10-minute shower break in their pods, cameras off obviously. After that, it was time for history class. A chair and desk came out of the wall in front of him.

A panel next to him opened to reveal his books and pencils.

The teacher reviewed their homework, reading about life in 12th century England. Then she gave a short lecture on castle architecture. After that, they walked through the famous Dover Castle. It was dark and cold. Aziz was happy that he was really safe in his pod. Of course, it was amazing that they could have trips to any time or place in the world! None of it was real, so most of the danger was eliminated!

That was one problem with the virtual world. Nothing was real. You couldn't even be sure what people looked like. Almost everyone used avatars. Some were clearly fake. He sometimes used a cute blue penguin avatar and for literature class, he had a William Shakespeare avatar. Even the realistic avatars had filters to make people look better. Filters made your skin smooth, your eyes big, your nose smaller, your body fitter. Anything was possible.

At that moment, a green message blinked on his screen. It was a private message from Hinata, his girl friend, "Are we still on for tonight, Zee-Zee?" Her avatar was very cute. It had long brown hair and green eyes. The eyes were too big to be real, like an anime cartoon character's. It actually looked very good on her. Her face had a sweet smile and she was wearing large pink glasses and a heart sticker on her cheek. She was very attractive.

"Of course, Hin-Hin," he responded with a smiling-face emoji. But he had a doubt. There was something he needed to ask her.

· · ● · ● · ● · ·

That night, Aziz and Hinata took a walk on the beach in southern California. Aziz was in his gym avatar and Hinata appeared as her avatar with big eyes. They both walked along the water, watching the sunset and eating cotton candy. Even though they were both still at home in their pods, all the sights, sounds, and smells felt real.

"The beach this morning in PE class was so beautiful, I wanted to take a romantic beach walk with you," Hinata said.

Aziz laughed nervously. "I want to ask you to do something."

"What is it?" Hinata asked, sounding nervous as well..

"I want to meet you." Aziz had never left his pod but he felt ready now. "After 6 months of dating, I think it's time. Don't you?"

Hinata's avatar started crying. "Don't you like our dates?" she asked.

Aziz tried to comfort her. "Of course, I do, Hin-hin. I'm having a great time. I just think it's time for more."

Hinata looked upset, "Is that all you care about?"

"I don't mean like that," Aziz said. "But don't you want to hear my real voice? Actually walk next to me?"

"I don't know. I just don't know. My parents said we shouldn't meet for a year," she said sniffing.

Parents. Another thing that made Hinata unique. Children hadn't been born the old way for decades. So people didn't get married or have kids any more. Still, there were couples looking to 'adopt' lonely kids like Hinata. Hinata's parents' were an old couple from the days where this kind of thing was normal. Her parents actually lived in a shared pod! At least, that's what Hinata claimed. She had dinner with them once a week and shared what was happening at school with them. They watched her in the school play and concerts. Sometimes they called her to tell her they loved her. When she got said, she could call them. It made her feel less lonely. And as they learned in their history class, this was normal for most of human history.

Before Aziz met Hinata, he didn't care about that. Life in the pod was great. Besides school, he could do whatever he wanted: watch old movies, play video games, travel the world, and hang out with his friends, including Hinata. In the old days, people were limited. Not everyone lives near a beach. Not everyone has mountains. Poor people couldn't do as much as the rich. Now everyone could do everything in their pod!

But he really wanted to meet Hinata. Of course, he had never left his pod before. He didn't know what the real world was like. Michael, his best friend, was the only person he knew who had left the pod!

As if reading his mind, Hinata said, "I've never even left my pod. Is it dangerous out there?"

Aziz reassured her. "No, it's safe. We can walk on the street or the park. I think there are real cafés too." Aziz wasn't actually sure. He tried to sound confident though.

"What if you don't like me? What if I don't like you?" she said, worried.

"Hin-hin, don't be like that!" he said. "How about this? What if we just show our real faces?"

"No avatar?" she said.

"No avatar, no filter. Just our real faces. I want to know what you look like. Don't you?"

"Maybe," she said. "Let me think about it. OK, Zee-zee?"

• • • • ● • ● • • •

His friend Michael laughed when Aziz told him about the conversation.

Michael's avatar was from an old movie, *The Godfather*. The avatar looked like a character from the movie. Michael's avatar wore a crisp black suit, with short slick dark hair.

They had watched another classic movie about the Mafia, *Goodfellas*, in a VR movie theatre. Now they were eating hot dogs and ice cream in a classic American restaurant. They had an AI Construct acting like a waitress to make the restaurant feel more real.

"What if she says no? What if she doesn't want to meet?" Michael asked Aziz.

"I don't know," Aziz said. "I'm not like you. It's hard to meet girls in the pod." Michael was always meeting girls in the real world. Aziz didn't know how or where he found them. He didn't know so many people left their pods.

"Are you scared to meet her?" Michael asked.

Aziz thought for a second. "Maybe," he said, "What if she doesn't like me? What if she thinks I'm ugly. Or being in person is just weird!"

"Why don't you start with faces? Ask her to turn off her avatar?"

"You know, I asked her that today, but she got upset and cried."

Michael's expression turned serious. "That could mean one of two things. Either she doesn't look like her avatar at all or …"

"Don't say it!" It was something Aziz had wondered himself.

Michael said it anyway, "She's an AI Construct. She doesn't have a real face. She can't leave the pod."

Aziz looked angry. "That's crazy."

"Really? Does it matter if she's an AI Construct? You said you care about her." Michael said.

"I can't love a computer. Besides, I can tell the difference." Aziz pointed at the waiter behind the counter who'd been cleaning the same glass for the last 20 minutes.

Michael laughed. "You know what people say. Not all the constructs are labelled. Some are pretty advanced. Like the pod computers. Hey, you could be AI. I never met you before!"

"That's ridiculous," Aziz shouted and shut down the cameras.

But now he had a doubt. What if Hinata wasn't real? What if Michael wasn't real? How would he really know. What if Aziz was the last human being on Earth.

He had to find out. He knew Hinata's address from her school form. He asked Alvin to get him street clothes. Then he opened the door to his pod and stepped outside for the first time.

Glossary

AI: Artificial Intelligence, computers that are capable of thinking like humans

anime: a cartoon style that is popular in Japan. Characters often have big eyes and act very dramatically

avatar: an image that represents a person on a computer website or other places

decade: ten years

PE: short for Physical Education, a class in school where students exercise and do sports

pod: a small room or one unit out of many

slick: smooth because the person used oil

VR: short for Virtual Reality, computer technology that makes you feel like the computer images are real

After You Read

1. What is a pod?

2. Describe daily life in the pods.

3. What are the advantages of school in this story? Are there any drawbacks?

4. Describe Hinata and Aziz's relationship.

5. What does Aziz want to do with Hinata?

6. What does she think of this?

7. What are families like in this world?

8. Why do you think people don't go outside much anymore in this world?

9. Is this a story of a utopia, an ideal future? Or a dystopia, a terrible future?

10. What are the positive and negative aspects of this world?

11. What other parts of this world could be different from our world today?

12. What parts of this future world are similar to ours?

13. Have you ever used ChatGPT or another AI program?

14. Will AI ever get so smart that we won't be able to tell the difference between computers and people?

Writing

Write what happens next?

- What happens to Aziz?

- Does he see other people?

- Does he do anything interesting?

- Does he visit Hinata?

- What does she look like?

- How does she react to him?

- How does he react to her?

More Readers

Baby Shopping
Changes
Empathy
English Class on Mars
Ghost in My Room
Magic Employment Agency
Rebirth
Attack of the Sleep Demon
The AI Therapist
Thought Police
Time Travel Research: Genghis Khan
Virtual Unreality

AlphabetPublish.com/Book-Category/
Graded-Reader